SPOTLIGHT ON POETRY

Poems Around the World 2

Contents

Collected by Brian Moses and David Orme

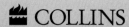

COLLINS

Acknowledgements

Whilst every effort has been made to contact the copyright-holders and to secure the necessary permission to reprint these selections, this has not proved to be possible in every case.

'Don't Call Alligator Long-Mouth Till You Cross River' by John Agard from The Puffin Book of Twentieth-Century Children's Verse, edited by Brian Patten (Viking/Puffin, 1991); 'Gilbert' by Pauline Stewart, reprinted by permission of the author; 'Hurricane' by Dionne Brand from A Caribbean Dozen, edited by John Agard and Grace Nichols (Walker Books, 1994); 'Holi, Festival of Colour' by Punitha Perinparaja from What a Wonderful Day!, edited by Tony Bradman (Puffin, 1990); 'I'd Like to Squeeze' by John Agard from Get Back Pimple (Viking/Puffin, 1996), reprinted by kind permission of the author c/o Caroline Sheldon Literary Agency; 'The Friday Night Smell' by Marc Matthews from I Like That Stuff: Poems from Many Cultures, edited by Morag Styles (Cambridge University Press, 1984); 'Silent, but...' by Tsuboi Shigeji from The Penguin Book of Japanese Verse, translated by Geoffrey Bownas and Anthony Thwaite (Penguin Books, 1964), translation and introduction copyright © Geoffrey Bownas and Anthony Thwaite, 1964.

The publishers would be pleased to rectify any omissions in the above list brought to their notice at the earliest opportunity.

Published by Collins Educational
An imprint of HarperCollinsPublishers
77-85 Fulham Palace Road
Hammersmith
London W6 8JB

www.CollinsEducation.com
On-line support for schools and colleges

Designed by Clare Truscott and Kate Roberts
Cover Design by Clare Truscott and Kate Roberts
Illustrations by Dorian Spencer Davies, Toni Goffe, Jan Nesbitt, Jeffrey Reid, Anette Isberg Rosijn, Jan Smith, Pam Smy, Holly Swain, Jenny Thorne, Joanna Troughton, Lisa Williams

Printed and bound in Great Britain by Scotprint

Collins Educational would like to thank the following teachers and consultants who contributed to the research of this series: Mrs J. Bibby (St Paul's C of E Primary); Jason Darley, Liz Hooley (Jessop Primary School); Mrs M.G. Farnell (High Meadow First School); Alison Lewis; Chris Lutrario; Lesley Moores (Princess Royal Primary School); Sheila Stamp (Castle Lower School); Sally Prendergrast (Brooke Hill School); Jenny Ransom; Jill Walkinton; Sue Webb; Michael Webster (Castle Lower School); Jill Wells (St Andrews CE Primary School).

Don't Call Alligator Long-Mouth
Till You Cross River

Call alligator long-mouth
call alligator saw-mouth
call alligator pushy-mouth
call alligator scissors-mouth
call alligator raggedy-mouth
call alligator bumpy-bum
call alligator all dem rude word
but better wait
     till you cross river.

John Agard

Give Yourself A Hug

Give yourself a hug
when you feel unloved

Give yourself a hug
when people put on airs
to make you feel a bug

Give yourself a hug
when everyone seems to give you
a cold-shoulder shrug

Give yourself a hug –
a big big hug

And keep on singing,
'Only one in a million like me
Only one in a million-billion-thrillion-zillion
like me.'

Grace Nichols

The Spider and the Fly

The spider said to the fly:
'Do look in when you come by.
It will be an honour.
I have a new home, new decor;
See the staircase and the curtains,
And the walls are hung with mirrors.'
The fly hesitated: 'I don't know . . .

I haven't seen anyone going up the stairs
That came down again.' The spider
Then resorted to flattery:
'You are looking absolutely lovely;
Your eyes sparkle like sequins,
and that glittering dress! . . .
I must say you are always busy
washing yourself and humming
As you fly that soothing tune.'
The fly winged past, flattered
That she had a new admirer.
'All right' she said and entered the web.

Mohammed Iqbal
trans. Munawar Syed

7

Oath of Friendship

SHANG YA!
I want to be your friend
For ever and ever without break or decay.
When the hills are all flat
And the rivers are all dry,
When it lightens and thunders in winter,
When it rains and snows in summer,
When Heaven and Earth mingle –
Not till then will I part from you.

trans. Arthur Waley

Haiku

In the ancient pond
I hear the sound of water.
A little frog jumps.

In the gentle night
Shrill chirrups of cicadas
Pierce even through rock.

Anon.

And My Heart Soars

The beauty of the trees,
the softness of the air,
the fragrance of the grass,
    speak to me.

The summit of the mountain,
the thunder of the sky,
the rhythm of the sea,
    speak to me.

The faintness of the stars,
the freshness of the morning,
the dewdrop on the flower,
    speak to me.

The strength of fire,
the taste of salmon,
the trail of the sun,
and the life that never goes away,
    They speak to me.

And my heart soars.

Chief Dan George

Gilbert

I hope that he'll not come again
that nasty Mister Hurricane.

You see that man is not polite
he sent farm animals into flight
and every time that man did sneeze
he bent back zinc and ripped up trees.
He took his claws and scratched the land
cleaned his nails and sprinkled sand.

I hope that he'll not come again
that nasty Mister Hurricane.

He ate us out of house and home
disconnected light and phone
and when he had enough of fun
left as quickly as he'd come.

I hope that he'll not come again
that nasty Mister Hurricane.

Pauline Stewart

Hurricane

Shut the windows
Bolt the doors
Big rain coming
Climbing up the mountain

Neighbours whisper
Dark clouds gather
Big rain coming
Climbing up the mountain

14

Gather in the clothes lines
Pull down the blinds
Big wind rising
Coming up the mountain

Branches falling
Raindrops flying
Tree tops swaying
People running
Big wind blowing
Hurricane! on the mountain.

Dionne Brand

Up in the Morning Early

Cauld blaws the wind frae east to west,
The drift is driving sairly;
Sae loud and shrill's I hear the blast –
I'm sure it's winter fairly.

Up in the morning's no for me,
Up in the morning early;
When a' the hills are covered wi' snaw,
I'm sure it's winter fairly.

The birds sit chittering in the thorn,
A' day they fare but sparely;
And lang's the night frae e'en to morn –
I'm sure it's winter fairly.

Up in the morning's no for me,
Up in the morning early;
When a' the hills are covered wi' snaw,
I'm sure it's winter fairly.

Robert Burns

Holi, Festival of Colour

Throw the waters, coloured waters,
Holi Festival's here.

Musicians playing, drummers beating,
Processions leading through the streets.

Joyfully children dance and sing,
Holi the colourful Festival of Spring.

Friends and relations all will meet,
Sweetmeats, balloons, for when they greet.

Throw the waters, coloured waters,
For Holi Festival's here!

Punitha Perinparaja

19

You!

You!
Your head is like a hollow drum.
You!
Your eyes are like balls of flame.
You!
Your ears are like fans for blowing fire.
You!
Your nostril is like a mouse's hole.
You!
Your mouth is like a lump of mud.
You!
Your hands are like drum-sticks.
You!
Your belly is like a pot of bad water.
You!
Your legs are like wooden posts.
You!
Your backside is like a mountain top.

Anon.

The Waves

Waves coming up: high waves coming up
    against the rocks,
Breaking, shi! shi!
When the moon is high
    with light upon the waters:
Spring tide; tide flowing to the grass,
Breaking, shi! shi!
In its rough waters, the young girls bathe.
Hear the sound they make
    with their hands as they play!

Anon.

Silent, But . . .

I may be silent, but
I'm thinking.
I may not talk, but
Don't mistake me for a wall.

Tsuboi Shigeji
trans. Geoffrey Bownas
and Anthony Thwaite

Prayer for Rain

Chauta we beseech you,
    we beseech you!
You have refused us rain,
    we beseech you!
The whole land has dried up,
    we beseech you!
Give us rain today,
    we beseech you!
We are concerned,
    we beseech you!

Have mercy on us,
    we beseech you!
Do not abandon us your children,
    we beseech you!
Do not harden your heart against us,
    we beseech you!
Send us rain,
    we beseech you!

Anon.

The Friday Night Smell

I love the
friday night
smell of
mammie baking
bread – creeping
up to me in
bed, and tho
zzzz I'll fall
asleep, before I
even get a
bite – when
morning come,
you can bet

26

I'll meet a
kitchen table
laden with
bread, still
warm and fresh
salt bread
sweet bread
crisp and brown
& best of all
coconut buns

THAT's why
I love the
friday night
smell of mammie
baking bread
putting me to
sleep, dreaming
of jumping from
the highest branch
of the jamoon tree
into the red water
creek

beating carlton
run & catching
the biggest fish
in the world
plus, getting
the answers right
to every single
sum
that every day
in my dream
begins and ends
with the friday
night smell of
mammie baking
bread, and
coconut buns
of course.

Marc Matthews

I'd Like to Squeeze

I'd like to squeeze this round world
into a new shape

I'd like to squeeze this round world
like a tube of toothpaste

I'd like to squeeze this round world
fair and square

I'd like to squeeze it and squeeze it
till everybody had an equal share

John Agard

Glossary

And My Heart Soars
summit   peak, or top

Haiku
cicadas   a long insect, able to make a rhythmic sound

Holi, Festival of Colour
Holi   Hindu festival of Spring

Oath of Friendship
mingle   mix together
without break or decay
without ending

Prayer for Rain
beseech   beg or plead

The Spider and the Fly
decor   the style of the furniture, wallpaper and ornaments
it will be an honour   I would be very pleased
sequins   small, shiny decorations sewn on to clothes
the spider then resorted to flattery   the spider paid compliments to help him to get his own way
winged past   flew by

Up in the Morning Early
a' the hills   all the hills
blaws   blows
cauld   cold
chittering   singing
drift   a pile of snow heaped up by the wind
e'en to morn   from the evening until the morning
frae   from
lang's   long is
no for me   not for me
sae   so
they fare but sparely   they can get little food
wi' snaw   with snow

31